Dream Around the World

by Deborah Eaton
pictures by Yu Cha Pak

HARCOURT BRACE & COMPANY
Orlando Atlanta Austin Boston San Francisco Chicago Dallas New York
Toronto London

Last night I had a dream. In my dream, I flew around the great, big world.

First I had breakfast with a family. I ate with chopsticks. Or at least I tried to!

Next I learned how to make a toy. My new friends helped me put it together. I raced with other children.

In the afternoon I went to a baseball game. We cheered for both teams. The game was a tie!

That night I walked on a beach and watched a turtle lay her eggs. I was as quiet as a mouse.

When the sun came up,
I was in the city. I knew
where I was.

Because this is my home and this is my family.

"It was a nice dream," I told my family. "Let me tell you about my dream around the world."